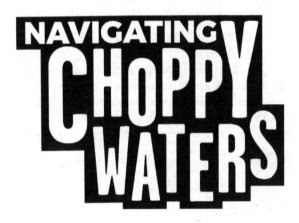

NAVIGATING CHOPPY WATERS

A BASIC TRAINING GUIDE TO UNDERSTANDING AND MAXIMIZING VETERANS' DISABILITY CLAIMS

NICOLE Y. EDWARDS, DO

purposely created PUBLISHING

NAVIGATING CHOPPY WATERS
Published by Purposely Created Publishing Group™
Copyright © 2020 Nicole Y. Edwards

Printed in the United States of America

ISBN: 978-1-64484-286-7

Special discounts are available on bulk quantity purchases by book clubs, associations and special interest groups.
For details email: sales@publishyourgift.com or call (888) 949-6228.
For information log on to: www.PublishYourGift.com

DEDICATION

This book is dedicated to my loving husband, Superior, who has and always will be my guiding light helping me navigate through the choppy waters of life. I love you beyond words, I appreciate you, and I wouldn't be who I am today without your love and support. Thank you for holding down the fort while I was voyaging from port to port on this journey. I will continue to show you how much you mean to me. Thank you again.

I also thank my wonderful children, Ellington and Tatum, who sacrifice their precious time with Mommy so that I can be all that I can be in my quest to provide them with a better life as we nurture them to become outstanding humans who make great contributions to the world. I pray that I have been an example of hard work and dedication that you can live up to one day.

I also thank my family: my parents and siblings who have always loved and supported me and been a constant pillar of love and support while cheering me on, not just from the sidelines but sometimes right by my side! Thank you all. I am who I am today because of you all.

I also thank Dr. Kre, Dr. Zee, and Dr. Samm: my best friends, business sounding-boards, mastermind partners, and fellow Millionaire-Mogul-Mamas. Without your accountability, affirmations, and firm nudging in the right direction, I wouldn't be at this point in my life, which is right where I'm supposed to be, at just the right time.

Thank you all, I love you to life.

TABLE OF CONTENTS

FOREWORD

As a seasoned Veteran's Service Officer with over six years of service working for a well-known, reputable Veteran's Service Organization (VSO), I understand firsthand that Veterans are a very unique subset of individuals, some with mental health conditions and physical disabilities, some who are homeless, and some who have had bad experiences in service and after discharge that can cause extreme trust issues. The United States Department of Veterans Affairs does a good job providing healthcare and benefits to eligible military Veterans, but due to the high volume of Veterans seeking assistance, and multiple claims that are submitted and processed on a daily basis, many Veterans can feel overwhelmed and can slip through the cracks when applying for their disability benefits and care. I can attest to this as I personally was stuck in the process and realized that this was not easy to do alone. I went into a VSO seeking to increase my disability compensation benefits after getting stuck in the process trying to do it alone, and the VSO officer told me that he was leaving the next day and it would take another seven or eight months before the next VSO officer would be hired and trained to be online. I told him that I was a quick learner and highly motivated and would love to work there helping myself and other Veterans through this difficult and often frustrating process. I started working as the VSO officer two weeks later with little training outside of a few hours course where I learned how to send in and upload information for Veteran's claims, but nothing about the order to file them, what to file, and what had a higher chance of being accepted. This is how I know you don't have to be a Veteran to help Veterans; you just have to be compassionate, considerate, and willing to find answers that you don't have questions to.

It has always been my recommendation for Veterans entering the VA disability claim process to find reputable medical professionals outside of the VA to assist them because the doctors at the VA are not given enough time to answer all questions and give the education and medical care at the one to two office visits you are given each year. Most Veterans have to go to the ER at the VA even for urgent care needs because it takes so long to get an appointment with their doctor, and calling for questions rarely affords the opportunity to speak directly to the doctor. Also, VA doctors are often limited in the amount of assistance they can provide with disability proceedings since the Health Administration is kept separated from the Benefits Administration. One day in 2018, in my search to learn more information to help Veterans, including myself, I was referred to Dr. Nicole Edwards to complete an exam and forms for me. She was not only able to assist me with a complete examination and completion of my claims, but she took the time to explain the process to me and answer my medical questions while showing compassion, care, and empathy.

In my position, while on active duty or in my retired status, I have met a lot of medical professionals, but I have never met a doctor who cared more for Veterans and was as passionate about her work. I was shocked to find out that she was not a Veteran herself as she was so understanding, personable, and comfortable working with Veterans where other people have been known to be standoffish and guarded when working with this population. Dr. Edwards is professional, knowledgeable, and caring. If she does not know the answer to something, she will find the answer and get back to you. She is thorough in her work and follows through on her word. I have seen her work long past her office's closing hours as she consults, educates, and helps Veterans, proving that she takes her time until the job is done and never rushes us or makes us feel bad if we don't "get it" right away. She places such a high value on education, and all the Veterans who have been referred to her say they learn so much from her about their medical conditions and about the disability claims process. I have listened to her explain the easily misunderstood and confusing process of disability claims to Veterans, including myself and the other staff at the VSO, in a manner that was easy to understand. She is truly the expert when it comes to VA disability claims, examinations, and nexus letters, and she will help Veterans get their highest rating possible while schooling them on the process so that they can go and teach other Veterans since most Veterans learn about disability benefits through word of mouth from other Veterans.

After reading *Navigating Choppy Waters: A Basic Training Guide to Understanding and Maximizing Veterans' Disability Claims*, I can truly say that Dr. Edwards has taken the convoluted, complex information that is available on multiple sites, pages, forms, and books available to the public but are hard to read, compile, and understand and put it into a succinct and readable format that is sure to bring clarity and understanding to Veterans all over the world. I often hear Dr. Edwards thank Veterans like myself for their service, but I thank

God for Dr. Edwards and her willingness to help Veterans everywhere. This book will definitely be lifechanging to Veterans and their families and will help bring clarity and guide Veteran's through the storm of applying for disability, compensation, and pension on their voyage to get the benefits they earned and rightfully deserve.

Martin Snowden
Veteran Service Officer

INTRODUCTION

My name is Nicole Y. Edwards, DO. I am a board-certified family medicine physician with over twelve years of experience—and over $300,000 in student loan debt! Much to the chagrin of people who think that all doctors are rich fat cats swimming in tubs of money in between practicing their golf swing and making deals with big pharma to make more money, many doctors are like me: looking for extra side hustles to pay back their student loans while trying to make a living. It was for this reason that I took a job working as a contract Veteran's disability claims examiner for the VA almost nine years ago.

Upon starting at the VA, I underwent "training," which consisted of watching a few hours of videos. The videos explained how to complete exams using a standardized questionnaire, and after I watched all the videos, I was able to shadow a nurse practitioner to watch how the examinations were done. Promptly after shadowing, I was given a stack of requests that needed examinations and completion. The onboarding process of getting my background check, fingerprints on file, badge, and security clearance to work at the VA actually took longer than the training I received! As I began attempting completion of the examination requests, I quickly realized no background on the VA disability process of ratings or how the Veterans actually file their claims was given. We were told that we should only have knowledge of completing the forms; this way we wouldn't be held responsible for giving any assistance or information on how, what, and in which order the Veteran needed to file the claims. The saddest thing that I've learned over the years is that Veterans aren't given any training on filing claims either! They often go into doing so with very little guidance, or the guidance they do obtain is from fellow soldiers or organizations with volunteers or lay people, and these people often have no specialized training either.

After a few weeks of seeing patients at the VA, I noticed that some of the other examiners would finish an entire day's worth of seeing Veterans in just a few hours. I began to ask how they were able to do that. That's when I was "taught" how to quickly finish exams without doing them completely and how to rush through the exams to finish them faster and be done. Contract examiners were paid per exam we did, so the faster you could complete the exams, the more exams you could do, and the more you got paid! I didn't understand how this was possible! I thought we were hired to help Veterans with their claims; what I later learned is that we were there to complete claims, but it rarely actually helped anyone.

Because I'm a type A personality and I don't like to mess up or be "wrong," I learned very early on exactly what was being asked of me and how I could do exams without having them sent back for addendums to add more information. Some examiners told me to purposely leave things out so that I could get addendum requests (since those were also paid for by quantity), but my pride would not allow me to do so, because an addendum request meant I didn't do something correctly. When I would get an addendum request for an exam, I learned how to call the rater (the person making the decision on whether the disability would be granted or not) and get more information on what was missing and why. It was frustrating because some raters would request one thing for an exam to go through, while others would request it differently. I was under the impression that the examination questionnaires were made to standardize the process, so that all of the disability ratings would be based on the same requirements, but what I learned is that there were still a lot of portions that were left up to the discretion of the rater. I used to tell Veterans, if you don't get the answer you want, file again, because you will probably get a different examiner and ultimately a different rater, so the next rating may be in your favor. If a rater was having a good day, then they may let the claim be accepted. If they were not having a good day . . . you get the point.

Over the years, I learned more information about VA claims, such as the order that claims had to be filed in to be accepted and the criteria the raters would use to base their rating decisions on. I was constantly seeing Veterans putting in the "wrong claims" (claims for conditions that had little to no likelihood of being granted), and I would ask myself, "Who is helping these Veterans put these claims in?" After a while, I started declining to do incorrect exams that I knew would be denied, and I would simply pull up the correct exam. For example, if a Veteran put in a claim for their leg, but the problem was actually stemming from nerves in the back shooting pains into the leg, I would decline to do the leg exam and I would do the nerve exam. I knew that Veterans and their representatives usually did not have a medical background, so how would they know that if they put the claim in for the wrong body part, it would be denied and then their claim would take longer and longer? It became more apparent to me that many Veterans would give up after years of being denied, and it started to seem like the system was broken both purposely and systematically so that Veterans would give up and stop fighting for their claims. I remember some claims taking over four years to go through, to be processed, or to even get an examination scheduled! The number of days pending an examination used to be printed on the examination request form; the longest I ever saw was 1173 days. Yes, you read that right! A Veteran waited over three years to even get an examination scheduled for a disability claim. And even after the examination was done, we would tell them that it could be eight to twelve weeks before they'd get an answer, and that if they hadn't heard back in twelve weeks to call the office.

I started to feel that the way Veterans were being treated was unfair, so I would do everything in my power to assist them. I'd tell them, "Did you know you can also claim this? And you can't put that claim in until this claim gets approved first . . ." Veterans would always thank me and ask why no one else had ever told them this information. I was even reprimanded on multiple occasions for "assisting" Veterans and giving them information on their claims. I was told to stop ordering and completing the correct examination and to just do the exam requested on the sheet. I would argue that it wasn't fair or right to the Veteran to prolong their disability process after they served their country. Though I did see a few Veterans who were "malingering" or exaggerating their findings, most of the Veterans I saw would actually minimize their complaints, and often felt guilty about putting claims in because "someone else probably needs this more than I do." My answer to Veterans was always the same: you deserve your benefits, and if you were injured in the service, no matter how small, you deserve to be compensated accordingly. Veterans and their families would often become tearful and express their gratitude, and many would ask if I too was a Veteran. I would answer honestly, "No, I'm not a Veteran. Both of my grandfathers were, my uncles, my in-laws, etc., but I mainly want to help you because it's the right thing to do." I could never understand why Veterans weren't given training or assistance in how to file for their benefits, and weren't even assisted in the process of getting their medical care set up. Do you know how many Veterans return home from being discharged and don't know that, because they were in the military for a certain amount of time and had honorable discharges, their medical care is covered and there are benefits that are set aside for them?

In 2016, about four years after I started working for the VA, we started to see a transition in hiring practices. The VA, like most other hospitals and healthcare systems, started hiring more nurse practitioners and physician assistants as full time employees. We would routinely argue with them, because exams that would take us one hour to complete would take them a few hours, or even days. We were unsure if the reason was because we were more seasoned since we had worked there longer, or if it was because our training as physicians meant we had a larger knowledge base, but we were not happy with where things were going. Soon after they were hired, the amount of time scheduled for our appointments with Veterans had to be longer to allow continuity across the board, so where I would usually see a patient in thirty minutes, I was being scheduled one or two hours. Many of the doctors complained because this was wasting our time and wasting the Veterans' time. Soon after, we started seeing less and less appointments being given to the doctors and more appointments being scheduled with the midlevel providers. We also were told that because of "budget cuts," many of the doctors were being phased out and no longer given appointment times. At one point, we would request a six-hour shift and only be given enough Veterans to fill a few hours. On November 12, 2017, I showed up to work and was told to go home, that due to budget cuts, we could no longer be scheduled, and they would call us and let us know when we could come back.

At that time, I had recently quit my full time job working at a hospital-owned clinic so that I could start my own privately owned cash-based clinic. I was working the VA examiner contract job to supplement my full time income, so imagine the blow to find out I no longer had a job! Fortunately, I had already booked a few clients into my private practice, one of whom was a Veteran. He brought me some VA disability forms to complete, not knowing that I had also worked at the VA on the side. The forms he brought me were the exact forms that I had learned over the years how to fill out. I did the forms for him since he was my patient (civilian doctors are allowed to complete the questionnaires also, we just don't have access to the VA records, or to the easier process of hitting send and having the forms be immediately sent to the raters, like when working for the VA directly) and he turned them in. Based on the forms I completed for him, he went from 30 percent service connected to 80 percent service connected! He was so happy that he sent me more Veterans. I filled out their forms and they had increases, and then they sent me their friends and co-workers, and before I knew it, I was seeing more Veterans in my clinic for disability form completion than I was seeing patients for medical care.

After a few months, the VA called me and many of the doctors back; they had suddenly found the funds that had been cut in the budget previously. I went back to working for the VA and we helped them get out of the backlog of examinations so they could finish their fiscal year and not be behind. A few months later, though, the numbers started dwindling again, and before we knew it, we were let go again, supposedly due to budget cuts. My mama always taught me, "Fool me once, shame on you, but fool me twice, shame on me!" so that time when we were let go, I decided to change the scope of my private practice to assisting Veterans with their whole person healthcare, mind, body, spirit, and finances, by offering them physical and mental health office visits and providing disability claims form completion and consulting.

Now, when Veterans ask me if I am a Veteran, I give this answer: There are two definitions of Veteran. 1) A person who has served in the military, and 2) A person who has had long experience in a particular field. So even though I have never been in the armed forces, I am a veteran in the field of Veterans' disability claims, and I am fighting the battle of helping Veterans get what is rightfully theirs. My motto is, "You fought hard for your country, and now I'm fighting hard for you!" I have now been helping Veterans with their disability claims through my practice for over two years, and I have about an 85 percent success rate in helping Veterans get their claims approved. I have Veterans coming from all over the world to consult with me on their claims, and I help them file their forms and provide them with medical knowledge about how their conditions are related to their time in service. I find myself teaching the same things over and over and over again, and I kept saying, "I wish there was a book out there to teach Veterans some basic information about filing claims," since I am only one doctor, and I can't help everyone by myself. That's where this book originated: I figure that if I can write some of the basic information I repeatedly discuss on a daily basis in book format, I can reach more Veterans and make more of a difference.

This book has been in me for years, but I didn't write it down because I was told by numerous people to be careful, that I would be blacklisted, that the powers that be would make it so that any claim with my name on it would be denied, so that Veterans would stop coming to me for help. But at this point, I feel like I can help more Veterans by putting this information in book format so that people can learn how to navigate the choppy waters of the Compensation and Pension process. I will still be available to give my knowledge, even if I am "shut down" from signing my name to claims. I hope this book gives you or the Veteran in your life the extra knowledge you need on how to file Veteran disability claims.

Chapter 1

WHAT IS C&P?

When I was in my residency training, I did a portion of my second year inpatient training at the VA hospital. When I wasn't on call every fourth day and night and had time to go to church, I would talk with some of the members. One gentleman saw my scrubs and said, "You work at the VA?" I told him I was training there, and he said, "Can you help me with my CNP?" I looked at him dumbfounded and told him I didn't know what that was. I asked him what it was and he wasn't sure himself; he just said that all Veterans want their CNP. I told him again that I wasn't sure what that was, but that I'd look into it. It wasn't until four years later, when I took the additional "side-gig" job as a contract examiner, that I finally figured out what he was saying! It wasn't CNP, he was saying C&P.

I walked past this department in the VA hospital every day on my way up to the inpatient wards, but never knew what C&P was or what it was there for. You'd be surprised at how many Veterans themselves don't know what C&P is, what the letters stand for, how to get it, or how it benefits them. Many Veterans hear about it from other Veterans who have been through the process or who are going through the process currently. The gentleman from my church who was a Veteran didn't know exactly what it was either! He heard of it from his friends, but they couldn't tell him any specifics themselves. I remember my mom helping my uncle fight for his disability from the VA for years before he got it, and I have helped many Veterans who have been fighting for their disability benefits for years; some older Korean War Veterans I have seen had been fighting for over fifty years.

So what is C&P? C&P stands for Compensation and Pension, and provides tax-free, direct payments from the Veterans Administration to Veterans and their dependents as a result of their service-connected disabilities, or because of financial need. This is the easiest way of defining it: disability benefits paid due to not being able to work to your fullest extent because of a medical condition that was either caused by an injury or was diagnosed during your military Active Duty service. This is similar in idea to Social Security disability, but it's for Veterans and is based on examination by a medical provider. Though the process seems simple on the surface, many Veterans choose to bypass or give up in the midst of the application process, as it can be difficult to get the disability approved if Veterans are not familiar with how to file claims or if they do not have the correct documentation needed to corroborate their claims. I've seen so many Veterans who tell me they are not "rated" or "service connected" and therefore not receiving any C&P benefits because they don't feel like being bothered by the process. For clarification purposes, "service connection" means you receive a rating percentage for a disabling condition because it was caused by or incurred during military service, and that rating percentage has an assigned compensation rate associated with it. Veterans can get anywhere between $0 to $3700 each month, and possibly more if they have dependents. I've also seen a lot of Veterans who make statements like, "I don't want to take C&P benefits or money because there are people who need it more than me, since my condition is not as bad as some other people." My response to them is, "If you were injured in any way or were treated for a medical condition in active duty, you need to be compensated for your time and your service, so get all you have coming because you deserve it!"

Please understand that Compensation and Pension is comprised of two separate parts; compensation is different from pension. When you are eligible for both, you are receiving compensation *and* pension services. VA pension services are needs-based benefits that are paid to Veterans with financial needs who meet certain criteria, such as not having a dishonorable discharge, serving at least one day in wartime, and serving for a certain amount of time (ninety days if you served before September 7, 1980, or two years if you served after this date). You also need to be over sixty-five, have a permanent disability, be in a nursing home or long-term care home because of a disability, or be receiving Social Security Disability Insurance (SSDI) or Supplemental Security Income (SSI). Many Veterans ask me if they can get both SSI and pension (or C&P), and the answer is yes. You need to understand that both of these services are provided by different entities, both have different eligibility criteria and different examining criteria, and are governed differently.

I typically recommend pension benefits for Veterans who meet the criteria and have trouble getting the compensation portion of C&P. These difficulties are often due to their records being lost or destroyed—either accidentally, such as in a fire or during transit, or purposely by people who didn't understand the value in keeping them, due to a lack of understanding of either what was in the records or the importance they carry—so that there is no way to prove what conditions were caused by or started in active military duty. The services from pension are paid for both the Veteran and their eligible dependents, like a spouse, and to survivors also. Some of the programs offered through pension outside of the monetary benefits are Aid and Attendance, where the VA will pay for a caregiver if they are needed to take care of the eligible Veteran (and this includes paying a family member as a caregiver also), and Housebound benefits for Veterans who are unable to leave their home. This also takes care of services like equipping their house or car to accommodate their disabilities, such as setting up wheelchair ramps, installing handles or safety bars on the walls, and equipping cars with special devices to better accommodate a disability. These pension services are available to Veterans eligible for C&P, so even if you can't get the compensation portion, you can still get assistance from the pension side!

While the federal government disburses SSI benefits for disabled eligible individuals and the VA handles Compensation and Pension benefits for Veterans who have service-connected disabilities, there is another entity that covers Veterans who were injured while completing active duty service or training: the Department of Defense. The Department of Defense provides disability benefits to active duty service members who have to leave the military due to an injury or condition that makes them unfit for duty. DoD disability compensation is calculated based upon service time, rank (basic pay rate), and disability rating, while the VA disability ratings are based entirely upon the severity of the injury or condition. The DoD offers severance pay, but please note that this pay will be deducted from any VA disability you receive later on until it is paid back in full. Veterans should always seek counsel before taking any severance pay to determine what their best course of action is for both their immediate needs and their future needs.

There are three groups that are involved in the Compensation and Pension process: the Regional Office, the examiners, and the raters. The Regional Office (often called the RO) is where all the claims are started and processed; they act as the liaison between the Veteran, the examiners, and the raters, all of whom together make up the compensation benefits process. When a Veteran wants to put in a claim for compensation, it is submitted to the RO. The RO then looks at the claim to determine if it needs an examination or if it is ready to be rated for severity to determine the amount of benefits. If the claim requires an examination, the RO sends a request to the examiners (called a 2507 request, which gives details about the type of exam needed, includes specific questions that need to be answered, and lists any medical opinions that need to be rendered or explained) and then sends notification to the Veteran that they have an appointment with the examiners. After the examiner completes the exam and renders a nexus opinion that will state whether or not the claim is connected to the Veteran's time in service (more details on nexus opinions will be given in chapter 3), it is sent back to the RO, and from there sent to the raters. The rater uses information from the Veteran's history documented in their service treatment records (you will frequently hear these records called STRs), the medical examination and opinion from the examiner, and the Veteran's current medical records to determine if the condition claimed is service connected and how much disability rating it is eligible for. Ultimately, it is the rater who makes the final decision about the percentage of disability that the Veterans receive for each condition, *not the examiner*!

This entire book is important for understanding and navigating this process, but what I'm about to say is the *most important* information in the book. Grab your highlighters, your bookmarks, your phones or cameras to screenshot this, fold this page down, or do whatever you need to do so you can remember where to find this info. Are you ready? Okay, here it is:

Compensation is granted for an injury or a medical condition that started during active duty, is chronic, and continues to bother you or cause impairment to the present day.

In the chapter on claims, I'll show you more details on how this works, but please understand that you can *only* get compensation for claims that started in *active duty* service or are the result of a condition that started in active duty service. This means that you *cannot* and *will not* get C&P benefits and payment for an injury or a condition that did not start in or happen because of active duty.

To help you understand this concept, I will give you some examples of conditions that are not eligible for compensation benefits or payments. If you injured your knee two years after you got out of active duty, or you hurt your back last year, or you just developed diabetes last month, those conditions will *not* be eligible for compensation. You can't put in a claim for a chronic condition just because you're a Veteran with a condition or illness. It is *only* eligible for compensation if it happened in or because of active military duty or service and is documented in your STR or civilian medical records.

A lot of people think a claim has to be for an injury that occurred in service to qualify, but it can also be for a condition that was diagnosed or complained about during active duty. So if your diabetes, thyroid condition, kidney condition, high blood pressure, acid reflux, fibroids, depression or anxiety, sleep apnea, etc. was first diagnosed during active duty, then you can claim service connection for them if they are ongoing and still causing some level of disability to the current day. Keep in mind, and please remember, that you will *not* be granted service connection for conditions that did not start during or because of active duty.

Why am I repeating this so much? It's because I see many Veterans putting in claims for conditions that are not eligible, which prolongs the process of getting service connection for the conditions that *are* eligible. This is also why you need to make sure whoever is putting in your claims understands this. Many times, Veterans give their entire medical record (from during service and after service) to their representative, or to another Veteran or someone who is trying to help, and that representative or helper will then take every single condition or complaint they find in the entire chart and put in claims for them. I've even seen representatives put in random "blanket claims" for general complaints or conditions that the Veteran may have never even had! This is not a good practice, as it slows down the process for the legitimate claims, which can then discourage Veterans from continuing to go through the process, as getting denials can be disheartening and frustrating. If Veterans understood the process better, they wouldn't have to waste time submitting claims that aren't eligible for compensation. Do *not* file claims for conditions or complaints that you do not have or have not been worked up for and given a diagnosis of. For example, if you do not have a diagnosis of sleep apnea from a medical doctor, nurse practitioner, or physician's assistant, don't put in a claim for it. Just because you have symptoms doesn't mean you have the diagnosis, and without a clinician workup, diagnosis, and documentation, you cannot get service connection. Do *not* file claims for conditions because it sounds like something you have. Just because you may feel tired and fatigued does not qualify you to have a diagnosis of, or get service connection for, chronic fatigue syndrome. All of the conditions you put a claim in for *must be* worked up, diagnosed, and documented by a doctor or health-care provider.

Another important thing to know, especially for people that served in the Reserves or the National Guard, is that the only conditions that can be primarily service connected are those noted during active duty. So, if you injured your back during an inactive time while in the Reserves or Guard, it cannot be service connected. Reservists and Guard members can only claim conditions that were reported either during deployments or during AIT, and they must be given a Line of Duty form and assignment or recognition to corroborate that the injury or condition happened during a time they were on active duty orders. If you had AIT and had an injury that you didn't complain about or go to sick call for during the AIT weekend, but then went to your civilian doctor the following day or week and it is documented in those notes that you were being seen for an injury that occurred the prior weekend during drill or AIT, you can use those notes to link with your AIT dates (found on your DD-214) and apply for an LOD in order to link the injury or condition to active duty service. If you are still in the Reserves or National Guard, you should also be sure to document any condition or injury you have that flares up during active duty orders or AIT. If it isn't documented during active duty, it will not be connected.

My recommendation for every Veteran (active duty, Reserves, or Guard) filing a claim is to take your service treatment records and write down every condition (physical or mental) or injury that was documented, diagnosed, and treated while in service. Be sure you also write down any abnormal blood pressure readings, lab findings (like elevated blood sugar, or kidney or thyroid function tests), and XRs or MRIs. Then take your current medical records and see if any of the conditions that started in military service are ongoing to the present day. If you find conditions in both categories, then those are eligible for service connection.

Another recommendation for all Veterans is to keep copies of your service treatment record to make it easier to review and reference. If you don't have it, request your entire file/medical record from the National Personnel Records Center. You can send them a written request, go to www.archives.gov to request it electronically, or contact the individual base hospital or clinic where you were stationed to see if the records are still available there. While you are waiting for these records, you can also start requesting your current medical records from your civilian providers, urgent care facilities, and the VA. Some of these can be found online, like on myhealthevet for your VA records, but sometimes these are limited to a certain time range (such as the last two years). To get the entire record, you may need to go to the facility, hospital, or clinic and request your entire file be put on a disc to review. Don't forget to also get copies of specialists' notes, surgical notes, radiology reports, and evaluations and assessments. You can also collect pharmacy receipts, *credible* buddy statements, personal statements, and any other documents you feel can help corroborate your claims and strengthen your case. Be sure to make copies of everything, both electronic and hard copies, so that if your records are ever lost or destroyed accidentally, you still have access to them. Since having this information can mean the difference between an approval and a denial, it is best to have your own copies of everything: records, claims, decision letters, etc.

Please use the two illustrations below to remember how service connection works.

Diagram One gives the process of getting service connection.

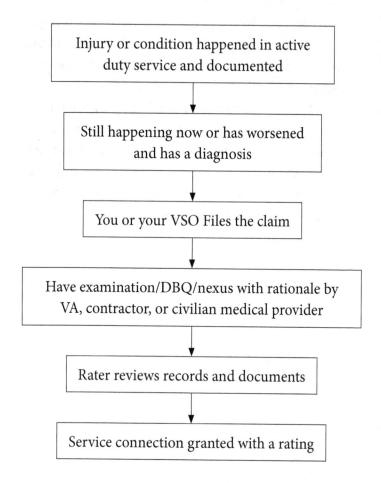

Diagram Two: Dr. Edwards' Service Connection Triangle uses a visual picture to show the three components necessary for a claim to be eligible for service connection. Just like the Fire Triangle that many Veterans are shown and taught during basic training that shows the three elements necessary to ignite a fire (fuel, oxygen, and heat/spark, and without any of the three parts the fire will not ignite), if any of the three parts of the service connection triangle are missing (1. Condition documented in active duty, 2. A current clinical diagnosis, and 3. A nexus with rationale from a doctor/healthcare provider), your claim will be denied as these are the mandatory things needed for service connection.

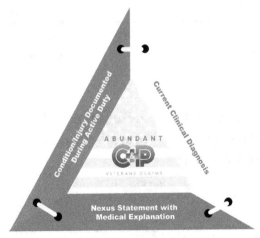

Service Connection Triangle

NOTES

Write down your local Regional Office phone number and contact information:

_____

_____

_____

Write down any questions you have about your conditions so you can find a healthcare provider or Veterans' Service Officer (VSO) to ask if the conditions are eligible for claims:

_____

_____

_____

Go through your service treatment records and make a list of all the conditions you see that you could potentially put a claim in for:

_____

_____

_____

Use the worksheet below to write down your list of conditions you think you would like to claim, and be sure they have the 3 components of the Service Connection Triangle:

1. Desired Claim

   a) Condition Listed in Service Records:

   _____

   b) Current Clinical Diagnosis:

   _____

   c) Nexus Letter with rationale written by:

   _____

2. Desired Claim

   a) Condition Listed in Service Records:

   _____

   b) Current Clinical Diagnosis:

   _____

   c) Nexus Letter with rationale written by:

   _____

3. Desired Claim

    a) Condition Listed in Service Records:

    _____

    b) Current Clinical Diagnosis:

    _____

    c) Nexus Letter with rationale written by:

    _____

4. Desired Claim

    a) Condition Listed in Service Records:

    _____

    b) Current Clinical Diagnosis:

    _____

    c) Nexus Letter with rationale written by:

    _____

Chapter 2

ALL ABOUT CLAIMS

Now that you've learned what C&P is, let's discuss the main place Veterans have problems: Claims. Eighty-one percent of WWI Veterans had their claims denied. As of 2017, 31 percent of claims were denied, and 60 percent of these denied claims were due to errors. These errors are often bureaucratic and systematic in nature, often caused by the very system that is supposed to help Veterans in the process or by raters and examiners that slow down the process. The rest of the denied claims were because the claims did not meet the criteria for service connection (see Service Connection Triangle from previous chapter), or the claim was put in incorrectly, either by the Veteran or their representative. Hopefully this chapter will shed some light on the claims process; understanding what claims meet which criteria can help speed up your claims process.

There are four different types of claims: Primary, Secondary, Aggravation of preexisting conditions, and Presumptive claims. Each has different criteria to be eligible for approval, and each needs to be filed in a specific way.

A Primary claim, also known as a direct claim, is a condition that was diagnosed or that occurred because of an injury during active duty service. This *must* be documented in the service treatment records or it will be denied. It requires that the Veteran went to sick call and was treated for the condition or injury, and that it was diagnosed and documented. We see a lot of trouble with documentation when Veterans are in combat zones and are therefore sometimes treated for minor conditions that are not documented. If the condition or injury was not documented in the records, it will be denied. I also see a lot of problems with this in certain military branches, such as the Marine Corps, where it was frowned upon to complain. Many Veterans have told me that they were told not to go to sick call unless a limb was amputated or they were dying, otherwise they would be treated differently, called names, or ridiculed. Unfortunately, because of this, many of these Veterans' claims are denied because they were not documented. This is why I recommend that all Veterans get a copy of their service treatment records to see what conditions were actually documented. The other place I see problems with these claims is with Veterans whose files or records were either lost or destroyed. Unfortunately, without documentation of the injury or condition occurring in service, it is almost impossible for it to be directly service connected.

Once the condition or injury is found in the service treatment record, the second thing that has to happen is that there has to be evidence of chronicity. This means you can't show that you sprained your ankle one time in service and expect it to be approved as a claim. You must prove that the condition it caused was chronic and continued to bother you through your entire military career, and even after discharge. You need to prove that it continued to bother you or would flare up from the time of discharge to the present day. If the condition is not chronic, it does not meet the criteria for service connection.

When filing the Primary claim, it is completed either online or by using the VBA-21-526EZ paper form, which can be turned in by mail or through your VSO representative, or brought to the Regional Office in person. When you fill out the form, list the disability you are requesting in the first column that says "current disability." The next column, which says "if due to exposure, event, or injury, please specify," should be completed only if there was a specific injury that occurred or if it was an exposure that caused the condition, such as to Agent Orange or radiation (keep in mind that if listing a specific exposure event, there is a list of the conditions that are known to be secondary to that exposure; see the section on presumptive claims). The third column says "examples of how the disability relates to service," and this is where you list more details of what happened that caused the condition or injury. The fourth column states "approximate dates disability began or worsened." If you know the specific date the injury or condition occurred, you can put that date here, though it is best to turn in documentation along with the claim to corroborate the contention. If you do not have the record, placing the approximate date here shortens the time it takes to find proof of the condition or injury when the Regional Office representative goes through your file to find documentation of the condition you're claiming.

Once you have the claim listed and have noted the date the injury occurred or the date the condition was first diagnosed and treated, the other portion of the claim is to prove that the condition continues to bother you to the present day, and causes some level of disability in activities of daily living or in your ability to work.

The next type of claim is a Secondary claim, meaning that the condition you are claiming was caused by a service-connected condition. For example, you may be taking a medication to treat a condition diagnosed during active duty, and that medication has side effects that then cause another condition. A few examples of this are headaches due to side effects of a medication taken for PTSD or nightmares, gastric ulcers caused by medication used for a service-connected joint condition, or erectile dysfunction as a side effect of medication taken for service-connected hypertension. An example of a secondary service connection for a condition other than medication side effects is radiculopathy that is secondary to a service-connected spine degenerative disc disease or bulging disc. The bulging disc can cause inflammation or can push against the spinal cord or nerves, resulting in tingling or numbness, and in severe cases can result in weakness, loss of sensation, or loss of reflexes or muscle control.

There are many other Secondary claims that can be filed. My best recommendation is to see a doctor who is well versed in VA disability claims and do a consult to see what claims you are eligible to file as secondary based off of your primary conditions. Finding Secondary claims takes some "connecting the dots," but for most doctors who understand the anatomy and physiology of the body, Secondary claims can be readily discovered.

Proving the Secondary Claim requires the doctor to explain and give the rationale about how one condition can physiologically cause the other.

A common Secondary claim I see Veterans trying to make is claiming their back condition secondary to their knees or feet. Though I understand the physiology of how a lower extremity injury or problem can change the way you walk (your gait), and this can cause some increased strain on your back and make your back muscles and joints work harder, which can advance degeneration, please understand that it is *very* difficult to get this service connected. Even with the best nexus, writeup, rationale, and even supporting journal articles, I have seen this claim denied numerous times. The times I have seen it approved would be when a specialist (such as a podiatrist for a foot primary condition or an orthopedist for knee or ankle primary conditions) writes the nexus and shows from their expert opinion how the foot, ankle, knee, etc. condition caused the back problem. Remember, though, that even when a doctor writes it up expertly, the final say is still ultimately up to the rater.

Another common Secondary claim I see Veterans trying to make is for sleep apnea secondary to PTSD. Though we know there is a *correlation* between the two, which means you often see both diagnosed together, there is not *causation*, which would mean that PTSD causes sleep apnea. If this were the case, then every single person with PTSD would also have sleep apnea. The cause of sleep apnea is typically a lack of oxygen due to collapsed airways that occur while you are sleeping. PTSD physiologically doesn't cause the collapsed airway, so you cannot use that as a cause to get sleep apnea connected. Though it is true that in the past many people did get their service connection that way, the raters and VA are now aware that there is no physiologic connection and causation, so you would have to get the sleep apnea connected some other way. You can find doctors that are well versed in sleep apnea, and they can help you find other ways to get your sleep apnea service connected if you can find ways to prove that you had symptoms of stopping breathing while sleeping (and also loud snoring, which is most times connected with it as well), but it has to be proven that you had the symptoms during active duty.

The biggest thing to remember when filing a Secondary claim is that you cannot file it until the Primary claim has been submitted and approved. For example, you cannot file for bladder leakage and incontinence secondary to a spinal stenosis or bulging disc until the lumbar spine condition has been granted. If the lumbar spine condition did not happen while in active duty service or was not documented, and that claim has not gone through, any secondary claims because of it will also be denied. This is where I stress the importance of putting in claims in the correct order and not just filing everything at once. You need to be able to show how your conditions are related to military service, otherwise they will be denied. Finding a doctor or healthcare professional to write a good nexus opinion *with a rationale* that explains how the condition is physiologically caused by or related to an injury or diagnosis that occurred in active duty military service is paramount to getting the service connection to be granted.

The next type of claim is a Preexisting claim that was aggravated beyond natural progression. A preexisting condition is one that occurred or started prior to service or was found on the entrance exam. For example: A broken finger while playing football in high school, a skin condition that may have been present since childhood (like eczema), or flat feet that were noted on the Military Entrance Processing Station (MEPS) entrance exam. In order to get a preexisting condition to be approved, you have to prove that it was aggravated beyond natural progression. This requires a doctor's knowledge to be able to state what the natural progression of a disease is, then you will need to be able to prove that your condition was worsened due to military training or service, and finally be able to prove that connection. In order to do this, you will likely need to prove that the condition worsened during military service at a faster rate than it normally does and that you required treatment for it, and then prove that it continued to worsen once you got out of the military (proving chronicity). For example: the natural progression of flat feet is that most people's arches flatten over time. However, this usually takes years to worsen to a degree that requires treatment. If your flat feet were noted to be asymptomatic when you entered the military (meaning they saw that your arch was flattened but it wasn't causing you any pain or problems), but then, shortly after you started basic training, or after you settled into a military routine where you did a lot of running, carrying heavy equipment, jumping, etc., you had foot pain that required you to seek medical care or go to sick call and they had to treat you with inserts, that is a progression of flat feet that is faster than the normal progression, and is likely caused by the increased vector forces you sustained during your training. Once a doctor writes this up and shows that there is at least a 50 percent chance that it was aggravated beyond natural progression, the claim can be approved.

The last type of claim is called a Presumptive claim. This is a claim for presumed conditions diagnosed in a Veteran in a certain group. The Veteran *must meet certain criteria*, and can *only* be approved for the conditions listed for that group. If there are other conditions you claim that are not listed, they will not be considered presumptive and will be denied. When the claim is presumptive, there is no burden of proof to show that the condition was incurred in service, like you would with a primary claim. You automatically get the conditions claimed as presumptive just because you had the exposure or were in the group, as long as you can prove that you have problems from that condition or that it is being treated to the present day.

Here are the list of groups and the conditions that can be claimed with each:

- Former prisoners of war who were imprisoned for any length of time and have the following conditions rated at least 10 percent disabling can be service connected for:

  Psychosis, any anxiety state, dysthymic disorder, organic residuals of frostbite, post-traumatic osteoarthritis, heart disease or hypertensive vascular disease, stroke and its residual effects.

▶ Former prisoners of war who were imprisoned for at least thirty days and have the following conditions rated at least 10 percent disabling can be service connected for:

Beriberi, chronic dysentery, helminthiasis, malnutrition including optic atrophy, pellagra, other nutritional deficiencies, irritable bowel syndrome, peptic ulcer disease, peripheral neuropathy, cirrhosis of the liver.

▶ Vietnam Veterans who were exposed to Agent Orange and served in the Republic of Vietnam between Jan. 9, 1962, and May 7, 1975, can be service connected for:

AL amyloidosis, B-cell leukemia, chronic lymphocytic leukemia (CLL), type 2 diabetes, Hodgkin's disease, ischemic heart disease, non-Hodgkin's lymphoma, Parkinson's disease, prostate cancer, respiratory cancers, soft tissue sarcoma (not including osteosarcoma, chondrosarcoma, Kaposi's sarcoma, or mesothelioma).

» If the following conditions became greater than 10 percent debilitating within one year of exposure to the herbicidal agent, then they qualify for presumptive claims as well:

Acute and subacute peripheral neuropathy, chloracne or similar acneiform disease, porphyria cutanea tarda.

- Atomic (Korean War) Veterans who were exposed to ionizing radiation; participated in atmospheric nuclear testing; occupied or were prisoners of war in Hiroshima or Nagasaki; served before Feb. 1, 1992, at a diffusion plant in Paducah, Kentucky, Portsmouth, Ohio, or Oak Ridge, Tennessee; or who served before Jan. 1, 1974, at Amchitka Island, Alaska, can be service connected for:

All forms of leukemia except CLL; cancer of the thyroid, breast, pharynx, esophagus, stomach, small intestine, pancreas, bile ducts, gallbladder, salivary glands, urinary tract, brain, bone, lung, colon, or ovary; bronchioloalveolar carcinoma; multiple myeloma; lymphomas other than Hodgkin's disease; primary liver cancer except if indications of cirrhosis or hepatitis B.

- Gulf War Veterans who served in southwest Asia and have a condition that is at least 10 percent disabling by Dec. 31, 2021, can be service connected for:

Medically unexplained chronic multi-symptom illnesses that exist for six months or more such as chronic fatigue syndrome, fibromyalgia, irritable bowel syndrome (IBS), any diagnosed or undiagnosed illness that warrants a presumption of service connection as determined by the secretary of Veterans Affairs.

» Please keep in mind that you must have been given a diagnosis of these conditions from a medical doctor, and that the diagnosis typically means that you have been checked for other causes or conditions that can cause those symptoms. I often see Veterans putting in claims for these conditions because they have symptoms that they find on Google, or because they have fatigue in general or joint and muscle pains, but they have not been given the formal workup or diagnosis from their physician. The first question on the disability benefits questionnaire (DBQ) for these conditions is "Does the Veteran have a diagnosis of _____", and if the answer is no, you will automatically be denied for that claim. Unfortunately, I see a lot of VSO workers putting these claims in for Veterans because *they* feel the Veteran has the symptoms or meets the criteria, but the VSO is not a medical doctor, and without the formal diagnosis from a medical doctor or provider, you *cannot* be service connected, even presumptively, for these conditions.

▶ Gulf War Veterans who served in southwest Asia can also be presumptively service connected for signs or symptoms of an undiagnosed illness that include:

Fatigue, skin symptoms, headaches, muscle pain, joint pain, neurological symptoms, sleep disturbance, GI symptoms, cardiovascular symptoms, weight loss, and menstrual disorders.

» These vague symptoms must also be worked up by your medical doctor, with no other condition or cause being found to account for the symptoms. This means that they have ruled out mental health conditions that often have symptoms such as fatigue, sleep disturbances, and headaches, or arthritis or other rheumatologic conditions that can have symptoms such as muscle and joint pain, weight loss, etc.

▸ Veterans who served at Camp Lejeune or MCAS New River for at least thirty cumulative days from August 1953 through December 1987 who had anything other than a dishonorable discharge can be service connected for:

Adult leukemia, aplastic anemia, bladder cancer, kidney cancer, liver cancer, multiple myeloma, non-Hodgkin's lymphoma, Parkinson's disease.

Finally, you can apply for a Presumptive claim (meaning you do not have to prove that the condition was diagnosed or incurred in active duty, or that you had an injury that was documented that caused the condition) if you are diagnosed with a chronic disease within one year of active duty release. Medical conditions are typically not abruptly caused (especially those that cause chronic disability), so the VA understands that these chronic conditions that occur within one year of discharge were likely manifested during active duty and just may not have been documented during the lengthy discharge process. It is very important, though, that you complete your discharge summary of complaints in detail so that any problems that may not have been diagnosed or documented during active duty will at least be listed on the exit evaluation, and thus will be examined during your Integrated Disability Evaluation System (IDES) examination that occurs pre-discharge. Many soldiers rush the process to get out and do not list all of their concerns and complaints, injuries, and problems; because of this, if they are not receiving medical care for these conditions in the first year out of service, they will not be able to get service connection for them later on if they were not listed or documented in the service treatment records during active duty.

Things to Keep in Mind about Claims

All claims (except presumptive ones) *must* have documentation that the condition was incurred in (meaning it happened during) or that an injury happened during active duty that caused the condition that is claimed. There also must be documentation that the condition is chronic, such that it frequently needs to be addressed by a medical doctor or provider following discharge. The more documentation you can provide, the better. This means that you need to be going to the doctor regularly, even for problems and conditions that could typically be treated over the counter. For example, many people buy over-the-counter creams for fungal infections like athlete's foot, jock, itch, or yeast infections, take over-the-counter antacids for heartburn or reflux, or take over-the-counter pain medication for muscle aches or joint pains; however, all of these complaints should be documented by your doctor or medical provider in order to get service connection, keep your current rating, or apply for an increase later on. I recommend that people see their doctor for each of their service-connected conditions at least one or two times per year (more frequently if the condition worsens or is bothering you more) to show that you are still being treated for it and that it is still causing some level of disability.

Use a knowledgeable VSO representative to file your claims, or, if you file them yourself, be sure you are putting them in the correct order. Remember, you cannot claim a secondary service connection for a condition that is not already connected primarily, and the primary conditions *must* be documented in your service treatment records. I see many Veterans applying for radiculopathy in the lower limbs secondary to their back, but the back condition is not connected yet. This will be denied, so please remember to file your claims in the correct order.

You need a diagnosis for each condition you file a claim for. Putting vague symptoms down will not warrant service connection. For example, you cannot claim dizziness; you need to have a condition that caused the dizziness, and that condition must be documented in your sick call notes or service treatment records. Do not file claims for a "condition," for example just listing a back condition or a hand condition, as this is not a diagnosis and you cannot be service connected without a diagnosis. Another reason it is imperative to have a diagnosis for whatever you are claiming is to be sure you are claiming the right condition. Many times, Veterans put in claims for lower leg pain or for a hip condition, but once their records are assessed and the examination done, we find that their actual diagnosis is a nerve problem from the lower back that causes pain to radiate down the legs. If you put in the leg claim and the first question is "Does the Veteran have a lower limb condition?" we have to write NO because it is actually a nerve condition. That claim for the lower leg or limb pain will then be denied, and if you are not aware that it is actually a nerve problem, you wouldn't know to then put in the correct type of claim.

Many service treatment records list "pain" of a specific area or joint in the assessment portion. For example, if you went to sick call complaining of pain in your back, the STR may list the assessment as "LBP" or lower back pain. Previously, you could not put in a claim for pain as a symptom. As of 2017, you can list pain, since that is often how it was listed in the service records, but it still requires a current diagnosis, such as strain, bursitis, or arthritis, to receive a compensable rating criteria.

A fully developed claim is one where you provide the Regional Office with the record showing the initial injury or diagnosis, the current records showing how the condition continues to bother you, and a nexus statement stating the current disability had at least a 50 percent chance of being caused by the injury or event in service or that it was incurred in service. The benefit of filing a fully developed claim is that by submitting all of the evidence and information needed to make a decision, the raters and Regional Office will not have to request or locate any of the information, so the rating decision can be made quicker. I've seen some fully developed claims go from filing the claim and turning in evidence to a rating in less than ten days.

NOTES

Write down a list of local VSOs who can help you with your claims:

_____

_____

_____

Go through your current medical problems and see if any are because of any conditions you were treated for in service:

_____

_____

_____

Write a list of possible claims you can make:

_____

_____

_____

Write down any knowledgeable doctors or examiners in your area who other Veterans have found to be helpful for doing examinations and nexus opinions:

_____

_____

_____

Write down any further questions or notes:

_____

_____

_____

Chapter 3

VA DISABILITY CLAIMS EXAMINATIONS

Once a Veteran puts in a claim for a condition, they will need a VA disability examination. This examination can occur at a contractor office such as LHI, QTC, or VES, or a private or civilian medical provider can do the examination; otherwise, the Veteran will be called in to the VA for a C&P examination. If the Veteran files a fully developed claim, with their records from service showing the initial injury or diagnosis, as well as current records showing how the condition is bothering the Veteran in the present, along with a medical examination and statement from a medical provider, the claim can be completed faster, because all the parts are in order to render a rating. One of the reasons claims may take longer to file is if the Regional Office has to put all of the pieces together (service records, current records, an examination, and a nexus opinion); this is why fully developed claims can get a response quickly, sometimes as quick as in seven to ten days. Fully developed claims do not guarantee that a Veteran won't be called in to a VA contractor or to the VA for further examination, however, because the rater and Regional Office can request an exam by their examiners at their discretion.

Many Veterans who get called in for a C&P examination are unsure why they are being called in, especially if they were recently seen by their VA provider for treatment for the condition. Something important to understand is that the Veterans Health Administration (VHA, where you receive your medical care, assessments, treatment, medications, ER visits, therapy, radiology, etc.) is different from the Veterans Benefits Administration (VBA). Many times these are both housed at the same location at the VA hospital, but they are very different departments, and they do not share records unless the VBA requests records from the VHA when a claim has been filed. I hear many Veterans say, "I just got new hearing aids for my hearing loss, so why didn't my rating go up?" Or they'll say, "I just had treatment for a bleeding ulcer, so why didn't my claim for GERD and anemia automatically go up?" If you do not put in a claim for a condition, the VBA will not know that your condition worsened or warrants a new or increased claim, so even when you are receiving treatment at the VA, you need to put in claims in order for the VBA to request your records from the VHA. Similarly, if you receive your care at a civilian medical office, you need to make sure your provider is sending copies of your office visits, including specialists' notes, radiology reports, medication lists, therapy or treatment notes, etc., to the VA so that they can be uploaded into your file. This is necessary to make sure that the VBA has *all* of your documentation of your medical care when you are putting in new or increased claims for conditions. Remember: when it comes to Veteran disability benefits and claims, if it is not documented in your medical records, then it did not occur. Be sure you read your notes from your providers to ensure the complaints you are discussing with them are being put into your chart in their entirety. If you complain of heartburn, burping, feeling something stuck in your chest, food getting stuck in your throat when you swallow, and food and acid coming back up when you lay down at night, and your doctor only writes "patient complains of heartburn," that lack of detail could be the difference between 10 percent and 30 percent service connection for that condition. If there are portions of your chief complaint or history of present illness missing from the documented office notes, you can ask your provider to write an addendum adding the rest of your complaint to the notes. You have to be your own advocate to make sure that your complaints are being documented and treated in order to get an adequate rating for your claim for that condition.

When you get called in for an examination for a disability claim, it can happen with any medical provider who is qualified to do that type of examination. For example: general medical claims (for joint and organ conditions) can be done by a physician assistant (PA), a nurse practitioner (NP), a general medical physician (MD or DO), or a specialist like an orthopedist or neurologist. Traumatic brain injury (TBI) exams have to be completed by either a psychiatrist, a neurologist, or a physical medicine and rehabilitative (PM&R) physician. Mental health examinations can only be completed by mental health providers, such as psychiatrists or psychologists, or, in the case of increase claims, a licensed clinical social worker can also complete the examination. A hearing exam for tinnitus or hearing loss can only be completed by an audiologist. A dental claim can only be completed by a dentist. Eye exams can only be done by an ophthalmologist.

Do not try to complete the examination on your own or fill out any forms on your own, as you *must* have a valid National Provider Identification (NPI) number or the claim will be considered insufficient and incomplete, and will be immediately denied. Also, if an examiner tries to do a claim that they are not qualified for (for example if a general medical examiner tries to do a mental health condition examination), then it will be denied and/or delayed while it is sent to the correct type of examiner. An examiner with high credentials, or one who is working within their specialty, is supposed to be granted more probative weight when it comes to the accuracy of their examination and medical rationale (explanation) or nexus opinion, meaning that if there is ever a disagreement between two examinations or opinions, whoever has the higher credentials will be the examination or opinion that is used for rating purposes. We will discuss this more in the section about disagreements and appeals.

Once you are called in for an examination, it is imperative that you go to the examination. If you miss an examination, you can be denied for a claim, or your rating can be decreased for a claim. It is also very important that you make sure the VA always has your correct address, phone number, and contact information. At your examination, your examiner will verify who you are by name and Social Security number. Then they will fill out a disability benefits questionnaire (DBQ). There are over seventy DBQs available for most conditions; for conditions where there isn't a specific DBQ, the examiner will complete a claim that is similar or which covers the same body part or area. If you submit a claim for a condition and it is not the correct examination for that specific condition, the VA C&P examiner or the contract examiner are required to do whatever exam you requested on the 2507. If you put in a claim for your arm but actually a wrist or hand exam is needed, the examiner can only do the arm/forearm examination. The first question on the DBQ is always "Does the Veteran have a diagnosis in the _____", and if the answer is no, the rest of the exam is almost pointless because it will be denied. But you will still need to wait for the results of that incorrectly requested examination before you can put in the claim for the correct body part. This is why it is imperative to have the correct diagnosis and to put the correct claim in, using a certified VSO or representative that is well versed in the C&P claims process.

The first portion of the DBQ is a list of the conditions that are pertinent to the claim, along with a medical ICD-10 code, and the date that the condition was diagnosed or when it started. This is another reason why it's good to have an actual current diagnosis, so that the claim can have the correct name, as the name for the condition you are claiming will not be changed. It can be updated if the condition progresses, but you want to be sure the initial claim has as close to a correct diagnosis as possible. You should also know that service connection requires a clinical diagnosis; you cannot list symptoms or "conditions." Without a clinical diagnosis, the examiner has to answer "No" to the first question on the DBQ (Does the Veteran have a diagnosis in the _____).

The next portion of the DBQ is a history where the examiner will ask you what happened that caused the condition, or how it was found or diagnosed. You can discuss what kind of workup you initially had and how it is currently being treated. You will then be asked about flare-ups of the condition and how it affects your function. When discussing flare-ups, you will want to give as detailed a description as possible. If it is a pain condition, you will want to describe the pain. Identify if it is throbbing, aching, burning, tingling, weak, stabbing, or tight like spasms; what symptoms go along with it, such as buckling of joints, not being able to grip or grasp, weakness, radiating pain, or nausea or vomiting during flare-ups; and where the location of the pain is. You should also discuss how often the flare-ups occur, as well as how bad the condition is on a day-to-day basis and how bad it is during a bad flare-up. When you are asked about function, the examiner needs to know what you are unable to do or have trouble doing because of the condition and what causes it to flare more, such as prolonged walking, prolonged standing, prolonged sitting, rising from a seated position, bending, lifting, carrying, going up and down stairs, sleeping, doing yard work, doing house work, getting dressed, driving, or taking care of yourself or keeping yourself safe. Remember, this is an examination to determine the level of disability the condition is causing, so they need to know how it affects your everyday life and if it is limiting in any way. When the VA and VA-contracted examiners ask these questions, they are not supposed to coach you or give you suggestions for how to answer. If you answer that you don't know or you can't find the words to describe the pain or loss of function, they will leave the question blank or say you answered that it does not cause pain or loss of function.

After the history portion, you will be given a physical exam *if one is warranted*. For all joint claims, you *must* have a physical exam done *in person*, and the examiner *must* use a goniometer to measure the range of motion. A goniometer is a handheld device that measures degrees of motion. The joint needs to be moved in all directions (for example, flexion, extension, rotation, and side bending), and it needs to be tested actively (meaning you move the joint) and passively (meaning the examiner moves the joint if it is safe and possible). Even if you are in pain or hurting, you need to attempt to move some, because if the examiner writes that you were unable to move due to a bad flare, you will get the minimum compensable rating for painful motion, meaning that a little movement, even when you are in complete spasms and moving only slightly through the pain, can actually get you more compensation than no movement at all. Also understand that you are being watched from when you walk into the room until you leave, and at some offices, they can even see you in the parking lot. So, if you bend over to pick up some paper or tie your shoe, but then suddenly can't bend over for the exam, the examiner can write that down and note that it looks like your pain is out of proportion to the exam, or that there are signs of malingering (exaggerating for purposes of secondary gain). If you are claiming that you can't bend your knee past 30 degrees for the exam, but then are able to sit in a chair with your legs completely bent and feet flat on the floor, it is apparent that you are actually able to bend your knee to between 70–90 degrees. My main point here is that you need to be honest with the examiner and during the examination, as most examiners have been trained to see when you are not being completely truthful.

The joint examination should also include testing for strength and a physical examination of the area. I see so many Veterans who tell me the examiner didn't look at the joint in question, but then reported on the exam that there was no deformity or swelling or tenderness to touch. If your examiner doesn't look at the joint or touch the joint, you should ask them why that portion of the exam is being left out and document their response. While not all claims and examinations require physical, hands-on touching, most joint claims do require a description of the joint and if there is painful motion or tenderness noted when they touch the area. There can also be nerve testing, such as seeing if you can feel something cold or something soft on your skin.

The next portion of the exam discusses things like what makes flare-ups worse, such as repetitive motion, and how much range of motion is lost during flare-ups. The examiner will have to test your range of motion multiple times (at least three times) to be considered repetitive motion. They will ask questions about pain in the spine or in the joint in question with weight bearing (while standing or holding a weight, or while pushing against gravity) versus non-weight bearing (such as sitting or lying down, when not holding anything, or movement with gravity or pressure eliminated) positions. They should touch around the joint or areas to see if there is any pain, swelling, crunching, popping, or grinding with movement (called crepitus). They may do some specific testing, such as testing your meniscus for your knees, or to see if there is any instability where the joint pops out or gets ready to dislocate with certain motions. They will then measure your strength, your reflexes, and in some cases your nerves. A back or neck exam should do a brief examination of the nerves associated with the area; this can be done by testing soft touch, vibration sense, temperature sensation, and even position sense or pinprick. A lumbar spine condition will always have a straight leg raise, which is best done by lying you flat on your back and raising your straight leg up from the hip to see if that causes numbness, tingling, or radiating pain down the leg and into your lower leg or feet.

Finally, the examiner will review your radiology reports, such as X-rays, MRIs, or nerve studies. It is best to have had an XR or MRI within the past twelve months for most joint conditions to see if there is any arthritis, or if the arthritis or condition has progressed or worsened, especially if this is an increase claim or a "future exam" to assess your current level of disability for an already service-connected claim. If there is no sign of any worsening, if it shows that you have improved, or if there are no records showing ongoing complaints (chronicity), then your claim rating may be lowered.

The last question asks how the condition impacts your work. This is where you need to discuss things like having to use any special equipment for work, any difficulties in doing or completing your job because of the condition, and if you have to miss work, leave early, or come in late due to the condition, including for treatment or appointments or because of flare-ups. You also want to discuss things such as if you need frequent breaks to use the bathroom, to get up and change positions, or to lay down or put your head down because of a condition. Furthermore, you want to discuss if the condition makes you more irritable and hard to get along with, and if the condition has caused you to get in trouble at work or to be written up.

The last section is a remarks section, where the examiner can write any extra information, write their nexus opinion, or show how the condition has worsened or changed since the last examination. A nexus statement is one showing how the condition or injury that started, happened, or was diagnosed in service is connected to the current condition.

There are five options for a nexus statement:

▶ Is caused by (100 percent chance that the current condition was caused by the in-service condition)

▶ More than likely (more than 50 percent chance that the current condition was caused by the in-service condition)

▶ At least as likely as not (*at least* a 51 percent chance that the current condition was caused by the in-service condition)

▶ Less than likely as not (less than 50 percent chance that the current condition was caused by the in-service condition, meaning that the condition was *not* likely caused by the in-service condition)

▶ Was not caused by (100 percent chance that the current condition was *not* caused by the in-service condition)

After the nexus, there should be a rationale where the examiner explains their nexus statement. For the affirmative statements, they need to show the medical explanation or mechanism of how the prior injury or condition caused or affected the current condition. For example: the current chronic kidney failure is at least as likely as not secondary to the service-connected diabetes, because diabetes causes elevated blood sugars, which cause damage to the renal tubules and renal arteries, causing damage to the filtration mechanism of the kidneys, resulting in diminished glomerular filtration rate, elevated creatinine levels, or protein spilling from the kidneys. Another example is: the current meniscal tear is more than likely caused by the injury that occurred in active duty, where he stepped into a hole while running and his knee twisted as he fell down, since twisting motions during a fall can cause damage and tearing or shearing forces to the meniscus, resulting in instability and pain.

This nexus with rationale, medical examination, and DBQ can also be done by your civilian medical provider as well, but they need to be well versed in how to fill the forms out correctly. All of the DBQs were originally found on the VA website, but as of March 31, 2020, the VA removed the public access to the DBQs so Veterans can no longer print them out and bring them to their provider to be filled out. The VA has its own reasons for this, including safety for the Veterans, as many bootleg and fraudulent companies were popping up completing DBQs online or over the phone—but as discussed above, a joint DBQ cannot be filled out without a hands-on physical exam. There is much discussion going on currently about the removal of the public access to the DBQs, as many Veterans and VSOs feel this is removing Veterans' access and their right to choose who completes their examinations. Keep in mind, though, that your provider can still submit the DBQ if they have them saved from previous exams, or they can submit their medical records, which can and should include all of the information on the DBQ, including the range of motion, strength, flare-ups, how it affects function, etc. Unfortunately, many civilian providers are not aware of all of the details the VA requires on the examination, so many Veterans will still get called in to a contract examiner or to the VA for an exam if the information given is incomplete or inadequate. Even if the Veteran's civilian provider fills out a DBQ and gives all of the information correctly, the rater can still request for the Veteran to go to see a VA contract examiner, as the VA reserves the right to corroborate the findings of any examination done by a civilian examiner.

Many Veterans have expressed that they do not like going to the VA or to the contractors for examinations, as there are multiple Veteran complaints of the VA and the contractors doing incomplete, short exams, and that they have been known to change the words or not write down all that was discussed in the appointment. Many Veterans also complain about the examinations with the contractors or the VA being shorter than ten minutes, and that oftentimes they do not do the entire examination. Although there are some DBQs and examinations that can be completed quickly, most of the examinations, especially the ones that require range of motion testing and repetitive use testing, take some time to complete if they are being done completely and correctly. When Veterans find an examiner who does do the entire DBQ like they are supposed to, they often are amazed and state that no one ever examined all of that, or ever asked all of those questions. The DBQs were originally made in 2010 to standardize the examination process so that *all* Veterans would get the same examination for the named condition, but unfortunately, many examiners do not complete the entire exam or have found ways to skip over certain sections so that the examination is not as long (remember, I was a C&P examiner for the VA, and other examiners showed me how to get through examinations quickly without doing the entire DBQ). This is detrimental to Veterans, as they often can get a higher disability rating if the entire DBQ is done completely and accurately and if they have the documentation to corroborate the claim. Veterans should *always* get a copy of the completed examination (which can be downloaded on myhealthevet, or you can request a copy from the contract examiner company a few days after the exam is done) and make sure that it was filled out correctly and in its entirety, and if it was not, or if you feel the information on it is not accurate, you can find your own examiner to do one and submit it as a supplemental claim for an appeal, or request an appeal (see chapter 5 for more information on appeals). If you are not happy with your examination at the VA or with a contract company, be sure to speak with the VA C&P supervisor or the contract company supervisor and submit a written account of the appointment and the complaints or problems that you encountered, so that it can be documented and addressed.

Many Veterans request for their VHA providers to complete DBQs or nexus statements for their cases, but they will decline that request; they are not allowed to do VBA claims while working as a VHA examiner, as it is not considered unbiased. The only thing the VHA examiner can do is document their findings and treatment plans in the VHA records, and those records will be requested by the VBA when you put in a claim. VHA providers do not give nexus statements, as that is the responsibility of the VBA examiner. You can request for your civilian provider to complete the DBQ and nexus, but they need to be educated on how to complete the exam and nexus correctly. Also keep in mind that certain wording and definitions of words are specific to VA disability claims and are different from the diagnoses in the general medical field. For example: ankylosis in the general medical field is defined as stiffness of a joint due to adhesions and rigidity, but VA disability examination training as written on the DBQs defines ankylosis as immobilization of a joint due to a disease, injury, or surgical procedure, meaning that there is complete fusion and no movement to a joint; basically that the joint is frozen in place. Due to the subtle nuances in the wording of VA disability claims, and the differences in their definitions from the medical field in general, civilian providers who are not aware of these differences may answer questions incorrectly or may not do exams correctly. Be sure, if you use a civilian examiner, that they are familiar with the VA disability exams and how to write a nexus statement correctly, with the correct wording and the right information that is needed, as a nexus must have a rationale or it is not valid.

NOTES

Write down any notes or questions about your VA examinations:

_____

_____

_____

_____

_____

_____

_____

_____

_____

_____

_____

_____

_____

Chapter 4

RATING DECISIONS

Once the examination and nexus opinion is completed, the rater gets the completed case (past records, current records, examination and DBQ, and nexus opinion with rationale), and it is up to them what happens next. If there are more questions, they can send the case back for further examinations to be done by the same or a different examiner, or to have more questions answered or clarified. Once all of the questions are answered, the rater will make a decision on whether or not to grant the service connection for a new claim, or to approve the increase request. The raters have certain criteria for each condition and its rating scale. If you meet the criteria, then you make that tier or level of rating. If you do not meet the higher criteria on an increase claim, then you will stay at the same rating. It is possible for your rating to be lowered if you do not meet the criteria that you previously met, which is why it is imperative to continue going to see a provider (this can be at the VA, the ER, your civilian doctor, or even an urgent care clinic, but make sure all records of the visits, complaints, treatment plans, etc. are turned in to the VA to go in your file) so that you will continue to show that you meet or exceed the criteria for your current rating. If the claim is new, the rater will approve the claim and give your initial rating based on the rating criteria.

All of the specifics of ratings can be found in the Veteran Affairs Schedule for Rating Disabilities (VASRD, also known as 38CFR Book C), which is a federal regulation that lists all of the detailed requirements for assigning military disability ratings. Each rating in the VASRD reflects the Veteran's level of disability, namely his or her ability to work and how much that ability is affected. The VASRD was created by Congress, and only Congress can change the rating system. The VASRD has different categories of conditions and body parts for rating, including joints, muscles, nerves, organs, etc. Each condition rating is assigned a four-digit code, and when you are assigned a rating, it will be based on the appropriate code. Since there are some conditions that do not fall into a specific code, they would be rated to a condition or code that is closest to the condition or the symptoms it causes; this is called an analogous code. For example, the headache

DBQ mainly has questions about migraines, and there is not a specific rating code for other types of headache, but if they are severe enough to cause a level of disability, other types of headache can be rated analogously as migraine headaches. Remember, it is up to the examiner to accurately record the information on the DBQ for the rater to make a rating decision. Please remember that the examiners (whether civilian, VA, contractor, etc.) do not have any say in the level of rating or amount of compensation you receive.

Even if a condition has worsened (either in your opinion or in your doctor's opinion) or causes you more pain or what you consider disability, it may not meet the criteria to be given a higher rating, since the rating is set by the VASRD. There are some situations and conditions where the maximum amount assigned by the VASRD does not warrant the level of disability compensation you think you deserve. For example, many Veterans request a high rating for pain and disability with their joints and trouble walking or standing, but oftentimes, the maximum that you can get for a joint is 10 percent, unless there is very limited motion of less than 30 degrees, or the joint is fused and cannot move at all. Sometimes there are other conditions that may not impact something as important as ambulation/walking that will nevertheless give a higher rating. It is important to discuss the rating scale with your VSO representative to see if you are already at the maximum rating before you apply for an increase exam, as multiple denials for increase can become disheartening and discouraging, and if you are already at the maximum rating, you cannot get a higher rating, no matter how many times you apply.

You cannot have multiple ratings and compensation for the same joint, muscle, or condition; you will receive one rating for whichever condition warrants the highest rating for that body part or organ. For example, you cannot be rated and receive compensation for both gastroesophageal reflux disease (GERD) and peptic ulcers. You will receive whichever gets you the highest rating. In this example, the GERD maximum rating is 30 percent if it meets all criteria, but a duodenal ulcer, if it is bleeding and there is resultant anemia, can have a rating of 60 percent maximum, so while you would not get both, you would get the higher rating of 60 percent for the ulcer. If you have claims in for both, it may show that both are service connected, but the lower rating will be 0 percent (non-compensable) and only the higher 60 percent rating will be shown and added into your overall disability rating.

Once a condition has been determined to be caused by or incurred in active military service, service connection will be granted. The rating can range from 0 percent to 100 percent, depending on the condition. Some conditions have maximum ratings of 30 percent or 50 percent, and sometimes only 20 percent; this is determined by the VASRD. Once a condition is considered service connected, they will then determine its severity and how much compensation it warrants. A common mistake for Veterans to make is to assume that 0 percent service connection means the claim was denied. This could not be further from the truth! If a claim has 0 percent, that means it is considered non-compensable, meaning the VA has admitted that the condition was caused by or during service, but you are not receiving monies for it. This can be for numerous reasons: 1) the claim is not causing you any problems currently, 2) you may not have documentation of the current complaints warranting current disability compensation (be sure to go to the doctor to have your complaints documented so you can get compensation for it if it is service connected), or 3) it may be a claim that has multiple manifestations, but only one can be considered compensable (for example, you can't get compensation for anxiety, depression, and PTSD; though you may have all three diagnoses, you will only get compensation for one of them and the others will be listed as 0 percent).

Most conditions have a minimum rating that is assigned when the condition causes some minor level of impairment, such as pain with motion, or ongoing problems that require medications and follow-up with a doctor. If you miss your VA examination for C&P but your records show that the condition started in service and continues to the present, you will often be granted the minimum rating for that condition. I see many Veterans that have had the same rating for many years, and even have treatment to show that it has worsened, but still have the same rating because they forget to put in the increase claim. It is very important that, if the status of your condition changes or worsens, you have the progression documented and then put in an increase claim for it.

Here is a short list of some of the most common conditions and ratings that I see in my practice. Remember, you can find the whole list on the benefits.va.gov website, or by Googling 38-CFR.

- Any condition rated at 0%: VA acknowledges it happened in service, but not compensable

- Headaches: 30%: occurs less than once a month, 50%: occurs more than once a month, are prostrating (make you have to lay down), and cause economic inadaptability (affects work efficiency or makes you miss work)

- GERD: 10%: common symptoms like heartburn, reflux, substernal (chest) discomfort, symptoms worse when laying flat, persistently recurrent (happens frequently) epigastric (upper stomach) distress and on medication; and 30%: more severe symptoms like trouble swallowing (dysphagia), weight loss, or near constant pain and distress despite medication and treatment

- Joints: 10%: painful limited range of motion, 20%: range of motion almost negligible (less than 30° flexion or less than 10° extension). It should be noted that service connection for instability or dislocation can be granted in addition to painful limited motion, but this is a different VASRD code and would require a specific claim to be put in for instability.

- Back/Neck: 10%: painful motion, 20%: limited and painful motion with abnormal contour of the spine or radiating pains down the limbs, 30%: limited, painful motion and affects work, 40%: very limited painful motion that limits work and has sequelae

- ▶ Diabetes: 10%: oral medication, 20%: insulin injection. This can have multiple secondary claims like cardiac conditions, diabetic neuropathy, kidney conditions, sexual dysfunction, hypertension, eye conditions, etc.

- ▶ Skin: 10%: 5–20% body area, 20%: 20–40% body area

- ▶ Scarring/Disfigurement: based on surface area or number of scars. Can also get 10% for painful scars.

- ▶ Mental Disorders: 10%: occupational or social impairment due to mild or transient symptoms, 30%: impairment with occasional decrease in work efficiency due to symptoms, such as depressed mood, anxiety, or panic attacks occurring up to once a week, and chronic sleep impairment with mild memory loss, like forgetting directions or recent events, 50%: impairment with reduced reliability and productivity with work and socially due to panic attacks or depression more than once a week, difficulty understanding commands, impairment of memory and judgment, or difficulty maintaining social or personal relationships, 70%: impairment with reduced reliability and productivity in most areas due to suicidal ideation and illogical speech or thoughts, near-continuous panic attacks or depression, impairment of memory and judgment, loss of impulse control, difficulty adapting to stressful circumstances, or inability to maintain relationships, 100%: total occupation or social impairment with delusions or hallucinations, grossly inappropriate behavior, including persistent danger of harming self or others, or disorientation and memory loss of names or occupation

▶ Peripheral Neuropathy: 10%: mild, 20%: moderate, 30%: moderately severe, 40%: severe with muscle atrophy

▶ Flat Feet/Plantar Fasciitis: 10%: mild, 20%: unilateral severe, 30%: bilateral severe, 50%: bilateral pronounced with extreme tenderness, Achilles tendon spasm, and pronation/supination not improved with inserts

▶ Sinusitis: 10%: 3–6 flares per year with headache and discharge, 30%: > 6 flares/year, constant sinusitis after repeated surgeries

▶ Rhinitis: 10%: > 50% obstruction from enlarged turbinates bilaterally or complete obstruction on one side, 30%: with polyps

There is an app available at http://myvabenefits.us that has all of the VASRD ratings in it; you can put your conditions in and it will show you what the requirements are for each condition and rating. It will also show you what the requirement is for a higher rating, so that you can see if you should apply for an increase if you have those symptoms documented.

A maximum rating of 100 percent can only be assigned when a condition is severe enough to completely hinder the Veteran's ability to find or maintain work. Combining multiple disability ratings together can be done to get a higher total disability rating; however, it is not added together like regular math. What has become known as VA math actually takes into account the percentage of the ability to care for and maintain one's lifestyle. With VA math, you are always adding together the percentage of the portion of ability to work that is left over, starting with the largest percentage first and then going to the lowest percentage. For example, if you have three ratings, 50 percent, 30 percent, and 10 percent, the total disability is not 90 percent (the regular addition of the three numbers); instead, it is 68.5 percent total, which would then be rounded up to 70 percent, since total disability is always rounded to the closest 10 percent. VA math is done by taking the amount of the percentage left over. In the above example, you would take a full bottle of liquid to symbolize 100 percent. If you then remove 50 percent of that liquid, you are left with 50 percent. If you then remove 30 percent of the leftover 50 percent, which would be 50 - 15, you're left with 35 percent. Then, if you remove 10 percent of the leftover 35 percent, you'd be removing 35 - 3.5, which would be 31.5 percent. You would then subtract the 31.5 percent from the total 100 percent, and you end up with 68.5 percent, which is then rounded up to 70 percent. It is very confusing and is sometimes easier to find automatic calculators on the internet!

Once you are at 100 percent service connected or above, you can also be granted permanent and total status, which means that your condition is stable and likely to last the rest of your life without improving. If you are not permanent and total, then the VA has the right to call you in at any time for a "future" exam or a review to see if your condition has improved or stayed the same. You can look on your decision letter, and if it does not say either static or permanent and total, then you can be called in for a future exam at any time, so be sure you continue to see your doctor and complain about your conditions at least one or two times per year to show that it still affects your ability to work. Even if you do not meet the

VASRD criteria for one condition at 100 percent, you can still be granted a total disability rating of 100 percent if you have one condition that is at least 60 percent rated that would make you unable to work any type of job, or if you have combined ratings where at least one condition is at 40 percent or more and the combination of all the ratings is over 70 percent and would hinder you from working at all.

This brings me to the topic of unemployability. Many Veterans apply for unemployability without completely understanding it. They feel that their conditions are bad enough to keep them from working, but they do not meet the VASRD criteria for 100 percent. If you apply for unemployability, all of your service-connected claims will be reviewed, and that will include going through your medical records and doing examinations for each condition that has not been deemed as static or permanent to see if they meet the criteria for their current rating or if they should be at 100 percent. What often happens in this case is that Veterans end up getting a decrease in their claims because they do not have the follow-up or severity documented to continue their current rating or to qualify for their conditions to be considered unemployable. My recommendation is to always make sure that all of your conditions are at the maximum allowed rating and that you have exhausted all possible secondary claims to get you up to 100 percent before applying for unemployability. If you have exhausted all other measures and you still feel the need to apply, be sure that your current conditions have been followed up on by your medical provider and that your documentation accounts for your current rating to lower your risk of your rating being decreased.

You can be granted a temporary 100 percent rating in some cases, such as if you have surgery for a service-connected condition and will be hospitalized for more than twenty-one days, or during recovery from a surgery or illness if the condition is severe enough to keep you from working during the recovery period. The temporary 100 percent rating for recovery is typically granted for three months; if your recovery will take longer than three months, you need to get special approval for an extended convalescent rating.

The main thing to remember for ratings is to be sure you have the documentation in your medical records, including statements from yourself or others, to corroborate your current conditions and treatment. You should also be aware of your current rating, and if you have any worsening, check to see if you qualify for an increase; if you do, be sure to file for an increase.

NOTES

Write down your current service-connected conditions and their rating. Are they at the maximum allowed rating?

_____

_____

_____

_____

_____

Write down any conditions you have that are worse than the rating given. Write down any information that you need to remember to ask your treating provider for to document your worsening conditions:

_____

_____

_____

_____

_____

_____

Write down any questions you may have:

_____

_____

_____

_____

_____

_____

_____

_____

_____

_____

_____

_____

_____

_____

_____

_____

Chapter 5

APPEALS AND DISAGREEMENTS

After you put your claim in and you get your examination and records reviewed, the raters at the Regional Office will give you a rating and you will be mailed a decision letter. This is a detailed letter that shows what claims you applied for and the status of each claim. It is very important that you review this letter in detail, as there is a lot of important information in it.

The first page will be a summary of your military active duty period and where and when you served. The next section is a detailed list of each claim you submitted and the overall outcome of the claim (whether it is approved or denied). The next portion (usually on page 2) is a list of the evidence that was used to make the decision. And finally, the last section is the reason for the decision. In the reason, the raters will tell you why they denied or approved the claim and the reason for their rating. Then, if it is approved, they will tell you what other things will need to be documented for a higher rating.

If you submitted private records, DBQs, examinations, or letters for your claim, make sure they are listed in the evidence section. Sometimes, not all of the documents you submitted are used, and those documents may have had important information that would have changed the outcome of the decision. Sometimes this is because the Regional Office did not receive all the evidence you submitted, or it was misplaced or overlooked. This is also why I urge all Veterans to make copies of all documents before you submit them, so that if they are lost you can resubmit them. If the documents you submitted were not used in the reason for the decision, you need to file an appeal.

Be sure you read the reason for the decision very carefully. The raters will list each portion needed for the rating decision in this section and then what information is needed for an increase. I have seen cases where the findings listed on the current rating decision are the same symptoms on the portion listing what is needed for an increase. If this is the case, you should have been granted the higher rating and should file a notice of disagreement (NOD) or a clear and unmistakable error (CUE).

If your claim was denied, the raters will also list the reasons for the denial. The most common causes for denial that I have seen are: 1) The condition was not incurred in service, meaning there was no documentation in your service records showing the condition. 2) There is no diagnosis, meaning that you have not been formally diagnosed with the condition or you put in a complaint or symptom instead of a diagnosis. 3) There is an incomplete exam or no nexus given linking the condition to service. 4) There was a lack of new evidence (if this was for a prior denied claim), so they continued the previous denial.

When a Veteran is not satisfied with the examination or with the rating decision, they have one year (twelve months) to file an appeal. Veterans can submit a NOD when they do not agree with a prior decision of a rater, and this starts the appeal process. As of August 23, 2017, there are three ways to file an appeal through the VA Appeal Modernization Act.

1. A supplemental claim can be filed, where Veterans can submit new and relevant evidence that the VA can use to make a new determination. Of-

tentimes this new evidence is a new examination, DBQ, or nexus opinion from another examiner, specialist, or doctor. This can also include buddy statements, personal statements, new medical records not previously used in the decision (this is why you need to review the evidence used, to make sure all current and necessary evidence was used), and even service treatment records. Many Veterans can acquire and find evidence in their service records that a condition was treated in service, and it's possible that the RO overlooked that evidence or didn't have access to the records. This is also why it is important to make sure the VA has copies of all of your medical records, including any copies of service records you have and any copies of current medical treatment, especially from civilian providers, urgent care clinics, etc.

2. A higher level review can be filed when the Veteran does not have any new evidence to submit, but feels like a rater with more experience or one higher in command needs to review the current evidence, as something may have been overlooked or not used to make the decision.

3. The final option is to make an appeal to the Board. This is the option that takes the longest amount of time, as you will have to wait for a hearing date, which can be months or years away. At the hearing, you and your representative will be able to plead your case before the judge, who then has the final say on your claim.

The type of appeal you should use varies between each case. It is best to work with a knowledgeable VSO representative or lawyer to decide which appeal option is best for you.

If you get a rating approved but it is at a level that you feel is too low, you can either submit more documentation as a supplemental claim proving how your condition is worse, or you can apply for an increase. There is no time restriction on new applications for increase, but remember that any appeals have to be made within twelve months.

NOTES

Write down any questions you have about appeals:

_____

_____

_____

_____

_____

_____

_____

_____

Write down any lawyers or doctors that you have been recommended to use for help with documentation for your appeals:

_____

_____

_____

_____

CONCLUSION

Over the past few years, the VA disability claims process has seen changes to make the process a bit smoother and not as time consuming. It is still a very difficult process to navigate, however, and there are many people who try to help based off of their knowledge of the process. Though the VA has attempted to standardize things so that all Veterans are afforded the same process, it can be subject to the examiner and rater. I always tell Veterans that if they do not get the rating they are seeking and it is for a legit claim (meaning it started in service or is due to a problem that started in service and continues to the present day), they should apply again, as they will likely get a different examiner, a different rater, or both. Veterans can also now take their service records to their own examiner, such as their private civilian provider, and can have the examination and record review done by them to be submitted and used as evidence.

The most important thing I want Veterans to remember is to document everything! If it wasn't documented in the service treatment records, it cannot be claimed. If your current conditions and their diagnoses and treatments are not documented, then they can't be used to help substantiate your claim. Be sure that you are going to the doctor frequently, even for conditions that you would usually treat over the counter (such as acid reflux, skin infections, headaches, allergies, foot muscle or joint pain, etc.), as these conditions may be able to help your claim if these same problems started in service or are being caused by a condition, or the treatment for a condition, that started in service.

Another important thing is to be sure you are seeing someone reputable and knowledgeable to help you put your claims in. Not every person that says they can help will be able to, so make sure you ask them about their track record and do your own research.

If you are still in the military, be sure you are going to sick call and documenting any conditions or problems you have in case it affects you later in life.

Remember that there are people and companies in the world claiming to help Veterans but actually taking advantage of them, so do your homework and make sure you are dealing with legit, reputable companies. Remember, a reputable claims company should not tell you that they can do your joint claim over the phone, as a goniometer has to be used to measure the range of motion, and they also need to be testing your nerves and your strength, as well as to physically examine you to see if you have any abnormalities (like swelling or deformities) that would render a higher rating.

All questions about VA claims can be answered on benefits.va.gov, though it can be hard to understand all of the information. I hope that this book has helped make the basics of Veterans' Compensation and Pension easier to understand and can at least point you in the right direction to find someone who can help you further.

To all families and friends of Veterans, thank you for sharing your beloved Veterans with us when they had to leave you to protect and fight for all of us, and for your love and support of Veterans, especially during difficult times as they deal with physical or mental conditions. And last but not least, Veterans, I thank you for your selfless sacrifice and service to our country; without you, we would not be who or where we are today.

NOTES

ABOUT THE AUTHOR

Dr. Nicole Y. Edwards, DO, is a board-certified family medicine physician, Veteran's disability compensation & pension examiner, concierge medicine physician, TV and radio medical consultant, and minister. She is a two-time Amazon bestselling author and travels the world internationally as a public speaker, health educator, and weight loss and wellness expert.

Dr. Nicole received her doctorate of osteopathic medicine from New York College of Osteopathic Medicine and also holds two master's degrees in professional counseling and marriage and family therapy from Oral Roberts University.

She serves as CEO and founder of Abundant Life Concierge Medicine, offering whole person healthcare and wellness for pastors, Veterans, and busy professionals. She is also the CEO, founder, and lead physician for Abundant C&P. As a compensation & pension examiner, Dr. Nicole completes disability benefits questionnaires for Veterans and helps them maximize their VA disability claims.

Learn more at www.drnicoledo.com

CREATING DISTINCTIVE BOOKS
WITH INTENTIONAL RESULTS

We're a collaborative group of creative masterminds
with a mission to produce high-quality books to position
you for monumental success in the marketplace.

Our professional team of writers, editors, designers,
and marketing strategists work closely together to ensure
that every detail of your book is a clear representation
of the message in your writing.

Want to know more?
Write to us at info@publishyourgift.com
or call (888) 949-6228

Discover great books, exclusive offers, and more at
www.PublishYourGift.com

Connect with us on social media

@publishyourgift